PEANUTS
The misfortunes of Charlie Brown

by
SCHULZ

HODDER AND STOUGHTON
LONDON SYDNEY AUCKLAND TORONTO

3

DON'T BE DISCOURAGED, CHARLIE BROWN. THESE TREE HOUSES AREN'T THAT EASY TO BUILD!

THERE'S OUR MAILBOX... WOULDN'T IT BE GREAT IF THERE WAS A VALENTINE IN THERE FOR ME FROM THAT LITTLE RED-HAIRED GIRL?

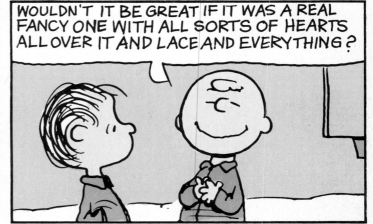

WOULDN'T IT BE GREAT IF IT WAS A REAL FANCY ONE WITH ALL SORTS OF HEARTS ALL OVER IT AND LACE AND EVERYTHING?

MAYBE IT WILL EVEN BE A SCENTED VALENTINE... IT WILL SMELL SORT OF LIKE VIOLETS OR A RARE PERFUME...

THIS IS SUNDAY CHARLIE BROWN... THERE'S NO MAIL DELIVERY ON SUNDAY...

14

✳ SIGH ✳

5

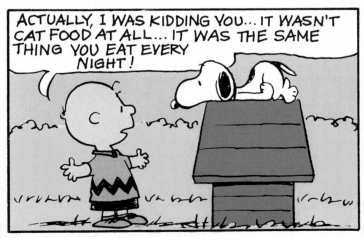

WHAT DO YOU HAVE THERE, CHARLIE BROWN?

I'VE WRITTEN A POEM..

REALLY? READ IT..

ALL RIGHT.. IT ISN'T VERY LONG..

SOME DAYS YOU THINK MAYBE YOU KNOW EVERYTHING...SOME DAYS YOU THINK MAYBE YOU DON'T KNOW ANYTHING...SOME DAYS YOU THINK YOU KNOW A FEW THINGS... SOME DAYS YOU DON'T EVEN KNOW HOW OLD YOU ARE.

THAT'S THE WORST POEM I'VE EVER HEARD!

A POEM IS SUPPOSED TO HAVE FEELING! YOUR POEM COULDN'T TOUCH ANYONE'S HEART! YOUR POEM COULDN'T MAKE ANYONE CRY! YOUR POEM COULDN'T..

WAAH!

SOME DAYS YOU THINK MAYBE YOU KNOW EVERYTHING...SOME DAYS YOU THINK MAYBE YOU...

SNIF

GOOD GRIEF!

SCHULZ

OH, COME ON NOW..BE REASONABLE!

I TRY TO DO MY BEST! I ALWAYS HAVE YOU SUPPER READY ON TIME, AND I ALWAYS TRY TO FIX IT JUST THE WAY YOU WANT IT..

BUT NOW YOU'RE GOING TOO FAR!

OH, ALL RIGHT..I'LL SEE WHAT I CAN DO... I MUST BE OUT OF MY MIND...

SOMETIMES EVEN I CAN'T BELIEVE HOW WISHY-WASHY I AM...

YOU WILL? GOOD...I REALLY APPRECIATE IT...

SO WHAT'S WRONG WITH WANTING TO BE SERVED BY A BEAUTIFUL WAITRESS?

2-27

9

10

CHOMP CHOMP CHOMP

HERE YOU ARE SNOOPY... YOU CAN HAVE THE REST OF MY DOUGHNUT...

BIG DEAL!

NOW, I'M SUPPOSED TO BE REAL GRATEFUL...

A CRUMB HERE AND A CRUMB THERE...

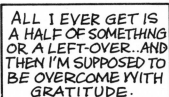

ALL I EVER GET IS A HALF OF SOMETHING OR A LEFT-OVER...AND THEN I'M SUPPOSED TO BE OVERCOME WITH GRATITUDE.

A PIECE OF THIS AND A PIECE OF THAT... JUST CRUMBS! I'M ABOUT TENTH-CLASS!

THE MORE I THINK ABOUT IT, THE MADDER I GET...

WHEN I DIE, I'LL PROBABLY GET THE SMALLEST ROOM IN HEAVEN!

HERE YOU ARE SNOOPY.. YOU CAN HAVE PART OF MY CANDY BAR...

BLEAH!

NOW, WHAT WAS THAT ALL ABOUT?

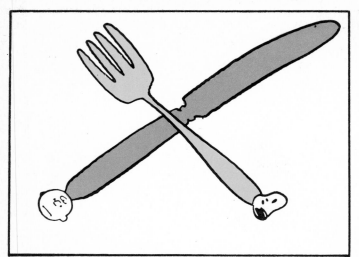

CHOMP
CHOMP
CHOMP

RAT'S I'M STILL HUNGRY..

MAYBE I CAN GET AN ADVANCE ON TOMORROW NIGHT'S DINNER

ANOTHER ADVANCE?

I DON'T KNOW WHAT I'M GOING TO DO WITH YOU...

$365 \times 5 = 1825$

ALL RIGHT, HERE YOU ARE, BUT I WANT YOU TO KNOW I JUST FIGURED OUT SOMETHING...

YOU ARE NOW FIVE YEARS AHEAD OF YOURSELF ON DINNERS!

SO WHAT'S WRONG WITH A LITTLE DEFICIT EATING?

SCHULZ

I SAW A MOVIE RECENTLY ABOUT A BOY AND HIS DOG

THEY WERE STANDING BY A LAKE AS WE ARE, AND THE BOY PICKED UP A STICK AND THREW IT INTO THE WATER, AND THE DOG SWAM OUT AFTER IT AND BROUGHT IT BACK...

I'M GOING TO HAVE TO STOP WATCHING THOSE MOVIES

I THINK IT WAS ONE OF THE BEST MOVIES I'VE EVER SEEN...

I KNEW YOU'D LIKE IT

SIP!

AFTERWARD, WE WENT TO THIS ART GALLERY, AND SAW ALL OF THESE WILD NEW PAINTINGS...

SOME OF THEM, OF COURSE, WERE QUITE HUGE...

THERE WAS ONE THAT WAS ALL DIFFERENT SHADES OF RED...

SIP!

I LIKE RED OF COURSE, BUT I'M NOT SURE IF I LIKE IT THAT MUCH, AND...

SIP!

HI! DRINKING LEMONADE, I SEE! HOW ABOUT LETTING ME HAVE A SIP?

DON'T BE STUPID!!

SIP!

YOU THINK I WANT TO SIP FROM THE SAME STRAW YOU'VE BEEN SLURPING ON?! GET OUT OF HERE!

ANYWAY, THERE WERE A LOT OF NICE PAINTINGS, AND...

SIP!

YOU KNOW, IT'S HARD TO TALK TO YOU WHEN YOU KEEP MAKING ALL THOSE STRANGE FACES!

SCHULZ

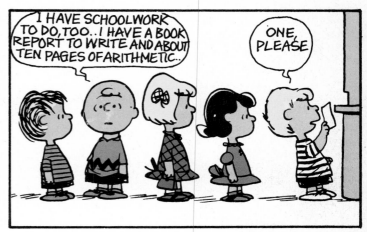

15

16

SIGH

LET'S SEE... TODAY IS THE SIXTEENTH, ISN'T IT?

VALENTINE'S DAY IS OVER

I'D GIVE ANYTHING IF THAT LITTLE RED-HAIRED GIRL HAD SENT ME A VALENTINE

MAYBE SHE DID SEND ME ONE, BUT IT WAS DELAYED IN THE MAIL! MAYBE SHE SENT ME A VALENTINE, AND IT DIDN'T GET HERE UNTIL TODAY!

MAYBE IT'S IN OUR MAILBOX RIGHT NOW...

I'M AFRAID TO LOOK... IF I LOOK AND THERE'S NOTHING THERE, I'LL BE CRUSHED.. ON THE OTHER HAND, IF SHE DID SEND ME A VALENTINE...........

I'VE GOT TO LOOK!

SMAK

I HATE VALENTINE'S DAY!

Z

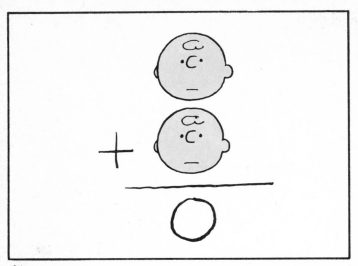

22

HMM..

SOMETHING IS MISSING, YOU KNOW THAT, CHUCK?

4-14

THIS IS OUR FIRST GAME OF THE SEASON, AND WE DON'T HAVE ANY OPENING DAY CEREMONIES...

I REMEMBER ONCE I SAW A GAME ON TV WHERE THEY RELEASED A HUGE FLOCK OF PIGEONS THAT SOARED UP INTO THE SKY, AND THEN FLEW IN GREAT CIRCLES AROUND THE STADIUM...WE NEED SOMETHING LIKE THAT

WE HAVE A SURPRISE FOR YOU... OPEN THE CAGE, SNOOPY..

THAT'S NOT THE SAME THING AT ALL, CHUCK!

23

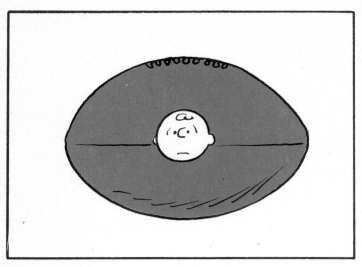

I'LL HOLD THE FOOTBALL, CHARLIE BROWN AND YOU COME RUNNING UP, AND KICK IT...

I CAN'T

I NEVER DO ANYTHING WITHOUT CONSULTING MY PSYCHIATRIST...

WELL, YOU GO TALK WITH YOUR PSYCHIATRIST, AND SEE WHAT YOU WANT TO DO... OKAY?

PSYCIATRIC HELP 5¢

I HAVE A STRANGE PROBLEM

THE DOCTOR IS IN

THERE'S THIS GIRL, SEE, AND SHE'S ALWAYS TRYING TO GET ME TO KICK THIS FOOTBALL, BUT SHE ALSO ALWAYS PULLS IT AWAY AND I LAND ON MY BACK AND KILL MYSELF...

SHE SOUNDS LIKE AN INTERESTING GIRL... SORT OF A FUN TYPE...

I GET THE IMPRESSION THAT YOU HAVE A REAL NEED TO KICK THIS FOOTBALL... I THINK YOU SHOULD TRY IT!

I THINK YOU SHOULD TRY IT BECAUSE IN MEDICAL TERMS, YOU HAVE WHAT WE CALL THE "NEED TO NEED TO TRY IT"

I'M GLAD I TALKED WITH MY PSYCHIATRIST BECAUSE THIS YEAR I'M GONNA KICK THAT BALL CLEAR TO THE MOON!

AUGH!

WHAM!

UNFORTUNATELY, CHARLIE BROWN, YOUR AVERAGE PSYCHIATRIST KNOWS VERY LITTLE ABOUT KICKING FOOTBALLS

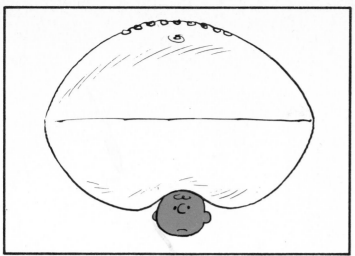

27

I MUST BE CRAZY TO WATCH THIS...

IT'S A BEAUTY CONTEST, CHUCK, AND FOR SOMEONE LIKE ME IT'S VERY DEPRESSING...

LOOK, THERE'S THE GIRL WHO WON...SEE HOW HAPPY SHE IS?

YOU THINK THAT'LL EVER HAPPEN TO ME CHUCK? NO WAY!!

I'M NOT BEAUTIFUL, CHUCK...I'M NOT BEAUTIFUL, AND I'LL NEVER BE BEAUTIFUL...YOU THINK I ENJOY WATCHING BEAUTY CONTESTS? I HATE THEM!

NOW I'M ALL DEPRESSED... RATS!

SAY SOMETHING TO CHEER ME UP, CHUCK...

WELL, I...

CLICK!

SMAK

HE'S A FUNNY-LOOKING KID, BUT HE KNOWS HOW TO MAKE A GIRL HAPPY...

SIGH

Y'WANNA HEAR SOMETHING FUNNY?

A WEIRD THING HAPPENED TO ME THE OTHER DAY, CHUCK... I HAD TO DELIVER A MESSAGE FOR MY DAD TO A FRIEND OF HIS WHO WORKS IN A BARBER SHOP, AND WHEN I WALKED IN, ONE OF THE BARBERS SAID TO ME, "WHAT CAN I DO FOR YOU, SON?"

THAT'S FUNNY!

SOMETHING LIKE THAT HAPPENED IN MY DAD'S BARBER SHOP ONCE A LONG TIME AGO... A MAN BROUGHT HIS GRANDDAUGHTER IN, AND THE BARBER THOUGHT THE LITTLE GIRL WAS A BOY, AND CUT OFF ALL HER CURLS! THE MOTHER WAS REALLY MAD...

EVERYONE WAS YELLING AND SCREAMING... BUT THOSE THINGS HAPPEN, I GUESS... AFTER IT'S ALL OVER, IT'S REALLY KIND OF FUNNY...

I WASN'T FINISHED WITH MY STORY CHUCK!

29

DOES YOUR KIND EVER THINK ABOUT LOVE, CHUCK?

WHAT DO YOU MEAN, MY KIND?

OH, I DON'T KNOW.. I MEAN, I GUESS I ALWAYS THINK OF YOU AS BEING SORT OF OUT OF IT...

THAT'S NOT FAIR... ACTUALLY, I'M VERY SENSITIVE..

OH, I KNOW YOU ARE, CHUCK... NO OFFENSE INTENDED... I APOLOGIZE... I REALLY DO...

FRIENDS?

SHAKE!

YOU TOUCHED MY HAND, CHUCK!

AND THEN SHE'D KIND OF GRIN..

☀ SIGH ☀

I'M WORRIED ABOUT YOU, CHUCK

ABOUT ME?

YES, I'M WORRIED THAT YOU'RE LIVING TOO MUCH IN THE PAST.. YOU HAVEN'T SEEN THAT LITTLE RED-HAIRED GIRL FOR OVER A YEAR, AND YET YOU KEEP TALKING ABOUT HER

MAYBE I'M LIVING IN THE FUTURE...MAYBE THAT'S WHAT WE CALL "HOPE"...OR MAYBE I'M JUST TOO WISHY-WASHY TO FORGET HER...

I DON'T KNOW, CHUCK.. I JUST HATE TO SEE YOU ALWAYS LIVING IN THE PAST... OF COURSE, I'D HATE TO SEE YOU ONLY LIVING IN THE FUTURE, TOO...

MAYBE, AS THEY ALWAYS SAY, THE TRUTH LIES SOMEWHERE IN-BETWEEN...

THE TRUTH IS JUST AS WISHY-WASHY AS I AM!

DEAR PENCIL-PAL
I GUESS BY THIS TIME EVERYBODY BUT YOU KNOWS THAT I HAVE A BABY SISTER.

I SHOULD HAVE WRITTEN SOONER TO TELL YOU, BUT I HAVE BEEN VERY BUSY. HER NAME IS SALLY. WE LIKE HER AND SHE LIKES US.

OH, OH!

IN A WAY, THIS HAS BEEN A GOOD EXPERIENCE FOR ME. I HAVE LEARNED A LOT.
AS EVER,
CHARLIE BROWN

SCHULZ

YOU'RE GOING TO BE PROUD OF ME, LUCY... I'VE DECIDED THAT THIS NEXT YEAR IS GOING TO BE MY YEAR OF DECISION!

THIS IS A LIST OF THINGS IN MY LIFE THAT I'M GOING TO CORRECT... I'M GOING TO BE A BETTER PERSON!

NOT ME... I'M GOING TO SPEND THIS WHOLE YEAR REGRETTING THE PAST... IT'S THE ONLY WAY, CHARLIE BROWN..

I'M GOING TO CRY OVER SPILT MILK, AND SIGH OVER LOST LOVES...

IT'S A LOT EASIER.. IT'S TOO HARD TO IMPROVE.. I TRIED IT ONCE.. IT DROVE ME CRAZY..

"FORGET THE FUTURE" IS MY MOTTO.. REGRET THE PAST! OH, HOW I REGRET THE PAST!

WHY DID I DO THIS? WHY DID I DO THAT? WHY? I REGRET IT ALL!

OH, WHAT REGRETS! WHAT REMORSE! WHAT ANGUISH! WHAT...

SIGH

YOU WANTED ME, MANAGER?

I SURE DO...

I THINK YOU NEED A LITTLE PRACTICE ON FLY BALLS, LUCY, SO IF YOU'LL GET OUT THERE, I'LL HIT YOU A FEW...

JUST TROT ON OUT THERE, AND I'LL HIT SOME HIGH ONES, AND WE'LL SEE HOW YOU DO...

WELL, GO ON! GET OUT THERE BEFORE I HIT ONE AND YOU HAVE TO CHASE IT!

I'M WARNING YOU... I'M NOT GONNA WAIT! I'LL JUST GO AHEAD AND WHACK ONE SO FAR YOU'LL HAVE TO RUN FIFTY MILES!

GO AHEAD! GET MOVING! GET OUT THERE BEFORE I SWING BECAUSE I'M NOT WAITING ANOTHER SECOND!

YOU'D BETTER START MOVING.. HERE IT GOES!!

OKAY, SNOOPY, YOUR SUPPER'S READY... COME AND GET IT!

OH, GOOD GRIEF!

I SAID COME AND GET IT! I'M NOT GONNA WAIT AROUND ALL NIGHT! NOW, HURRY UP!!

ALL RIGHT, IF YOU'RE NOT ANY MORE INTERESTED THAN THAT, I'LL TAKE IT OUT, AND GIVE IT TO THE NEIGHBOUR'S CATS!!

ⵌ SIGH ⵌ

SCHULZ

A FRIEND OF MINE AT SCHOOL GOT SOME GOLDFISH FOR HIS BIRTHDAY, BUT I DON'T THINK HE REALLY WANTED THEM..

PEOPLE BUY PETS FOR STRANGE REASONS

HOW DID YOU HAPPEN TO GET SNOOPY, CHARLIE BROWN?

WELL, I'M NOT QUITE SURE BECAUSE I WAS KIND OF YOUNG...

I THINK IT STARTED BECAUSE OF SOMETHING THAT HAPPENED AT A PLAYGROUND... I WAS PLAYING IN A SANDBOX WITH A COUPLE OF OTHER KIDS... I CAN'T EVEN REMEMBER WHO THEY WERE...

ANYWAY, ALL OF A SUDDEN, ONE OF THEM POURED A WHOLE BUCKET OF SAND OVER MY HEAD... I STARTED CRYING, I GUESS, AND MY MOTHER CAME RUNNING UP, AND TOOK ME HOME

IT'S KIND OF EMBARRASSING NOW TO TALK ABOUT IT

ANYWAY THE NEXT DAY WE DROVE OUT TO THE DAISY HILL PUPPY FARM, AND MY MOTHER AND DAD BOUGHT ME A DOG...

GOOD GRIEF!

42

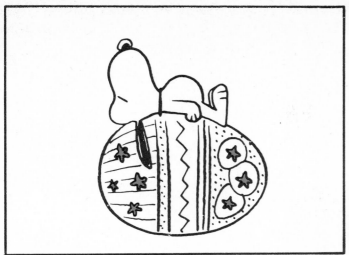

Official
Programme

Donation 25¢

HA! YOU DIDN'T THINK I COULD GET MENTIONED, BUT I DID!

I DON'T KNOW WHAT YOU'RE TALKING ABOUT...

THE SCHOOL PLAY! THE PROGRAMME WHERE EVERYONE GETS MENTIONED!

SEE? THEY HAVE THE NAMES OF ALL THE KIDS WHO WERE IN THE PLAY, AND THEY HAVE THE NAMES OF ALL THE ADULTS WHO HELPED WITH SCENERY AND FOOD AND THINGS...

WHERE DO YOU COME IN?

WHERE DO I COME IN? JUST READ THAT LAST LINE... YOU'LL SEE...

" SPACE DOES NOT PERMIT THE LISTING OF ALL THOSE WONDERFUL PEOPLE WHO GAVE THEIR TIME AND EFFORT WHEN NEEDED "

BY GOLLY, DON'T TELL ME I'M NOT IMPORTANT ENOUGH TO GET MENTIONED!

I'M COMPLETELY CONVINCED!

SEVEN O'CLOCK, SALLY... TIME TO GET UP!

GOOD GRIEF... I'VE GOT TO HURRY...

The Incas

The Incas were people who lived a long time ago in Incaland.

They had a highly developed civilization.

They would still be here today, but they lacked motel facilities.

SOME OF MY BEST TERM PAPERS HAVE BEEN WRITTEN BEFORE BREAKFAST!

HOW DO YOU LIKE THE SHOW SO FAR?

IT'S PRETTY GOOD I GUESS...

DO YOU COME TO THESE SHOWS VERY OFTEN?

NO, THIS IS MY FIRST TIME...

ACTUALLY, THE MAIN REASON I'M HERE IS TO REVIEW THE SHOW FOR OUR SCHOOL NEWSPAPER...

SCHULZ